WOLFGANG AMADEUS MOZART
(1756 - 1791)
SELECTED WORKS FOR PIANO
Compiled and Edited by Keith Snell

CONTENTS

Wolfgang Amadeus Mozart 2

Glossary of Compositional Forms 3

VIENNESE SONATINA NO. 1 IN C MAJOR
    Allegro 4

SONATA IN C MAJOR, K. 545
    Allegro 8
    Andante 13
    Rondo: Allegretto 17

FANTASY IN D MINOR, K. 397 20

RONDO IN D MAJOR, K. 485 26

TWELVE VARIATIONS ON *Ah, vous dirai - je Maman,* K. 300e (K. 265) 35

RONDO ALLA TURCA (FROM SONATA IN A, K. 331) 49

Execution of Trills . . . . Inside Back Cover

For supplementary study, a recording is available on compact disc, performed by pianist Diane Hidy (GP394CD).
Ms. Hidy's interpretations follow this edition closely as a practical example for students.

ISBN 0-8497-6203-0

WOLFGANG AMADEUS MOZART (1756-1791)

Wolfgang Amadeus Mozart was born in Salzburg, Austria, on January 27, 1756. He lived for only thirty-five years, but during his short life became one of the greatest miracles of music. The supreme genius of his music is unsurpassed in lyric beauty, rhythmic variety, and effortless melodic invention. The universal recognition of Mozart's genius has never wavered among professional musicians, amateurs, and the general public. In his music, smiling simplicity is combined with serious drama and sublime inspiration is contrasted with playful entertainment.

Mozart's first and only teacher was his father, Leopold Mozart (1719-1787). From his father, Mozart learned to play the violin and keyboard instruments, as well as to compose. His remarkable talent demonstrated itself at a very early age. Mozart may still be considered the most extraordinary child prodigy who ever lived. At the age of five, he gave his first concert and he had already begun to compose short pieces for the harpsichord and violin. Mozart's father was eager to promote Wolfgang as a child prodigy. For the next ten years, between the ages of six and sixteen, he traveled throughout Europe playing for royalty and garnering the admiration of musicians and music lovers. Along with his excellent performances and beautiful compositions, Mozart astonished listeners with his ability to improvise.

Mozart lived (between travels) in Salzburg and was appointed to the royal court in service of the Archbishop as Konzertmeister. In 1781, he moved to Vienna with the Archbishop's establishment. Due to Mozart's rash artistic temperament and egotistical attitude, it was difficult for him to successfully fulfill his duties as an employee of the Archbishop. He became resentful of his position in the court and was released from his contract by the end of 1781. In the following year, Mozart married Constanze Weber in Vienna, where he lived the rest of his life.

Leopold Mozart remained the stabilizing force in Mozart's life. Although Mozart was paid for his compositions and performances (and occasional teaching), he was never able to get away from lasting financial troubles. When his father died in 1787, Mozart was incapable of successfully managing his own financial and business affairs. He was continually requesting loans from friends, which he never repaid.

In 1791, while composing his final work, the *Requiem*, Mozart fell ill and became obsessed with the idea that he was writing the mass for his own death. He died on December 5, 1791, before completing the *Requiem*. The cause of death was registered as military fever, and later as rheumatic inflammatory fever. There have been posthumous rumors that he was poisoned, but there is no evidence to support this theory. Mozart was buried in a communal grave, in the custom of the day, at St. Mark's churchyard outside Vienna.

Throughout his life, Mozart never stopped traveling, performing and composing. In all, he composed over six-hundred works and wrote in nearly every genre and for every instrument. His large output includes: symphonies, serenades, and divertimentos for orchestra; concertos for piano, violin, and wind instruments; chamber music (quartets, quintets, sonatas, duos and trios); piano sonatas; operas and other compositions for the stage; masses, oratorios and cantatas.

The painting on the cover of this book is by G. Dagotis and
is titled *Portrait of Theresa di Savoia.*

GLOSSARY OF COMPOSITIONAL FORMS

FANTASY (also: fantasie, fantasia, phantasie): A composition in which freedom of structure and an improvisatory style prevail over conventions or restrictions of form.

RONDO: A form frequently used in classical sonatas for the final movement. It evolved from the French *rondeau* and follows the scheme RARBRA^{1}R. In this form, the rondo is similar to sonata form in that A and A^1 correspond to the exposition and recapitulation, and B to the development. The recurring section, R, is called the episode. Other versions of rondo form can be in ternary form, ABA, or in five part form, ABABA or ABACA.

SONATA: A composition for solo piano (or for violin, 'cello, flute, etc., with piano accompaniment) which consists of three or four separate sections called movements. The normal scheme for the movements of a sonata is:
1. FAST (Allegro)
2. SLOW (Andante, Adagio, Lento, Largo)
3. DANCE-LIKE CHARACTER (Minuet or Scherzo)
4. FAST (Allegro, Allegretto, Vivace, Presto)

The Minuet or Scherzo movement is sometimes missing, particularly in Mozart sonatas. The individual movements are subject to certain conventions of formal structure, which are followed with varying degrees of flexibility by different composers. The first movement is almost always in what is called *sonata form* (also known as *sonata-allegro* form); the second movement is often in sonata form or ternary form but may be in binary or variation form; the third movement is normally in ternary form: Minuet (Scherzo)-Trio-Minuet; the last movement is usually in sonata form or rondo form.

SONATA FORM: A term that designates a form frequently used for individual movements of sonatas. Since it is the form used most for first movements, it is also known as *sonata-allegro form* or *first-movement form*. However, this is somewhat misleading since the form is also used for slow movements or final movements. A movement written in sonata form consists of three sections as shown below. Closing themes and codas are not always included.
1. EXPOSITION
   a) first theme (tonic key)
   b) second theme (dominant key)
   c) closing theme
2. DEVELOPMENT
   Themes are developed and presented in new keys.
3. RECAPITULATION
   a) first theme (tonic key)
   b) second theme (tonic key)
   c) closing theme
   d) coda

SONATINA (also: easy sonata, sonatine): A diminutive sonata, with shorter and sometimes fewer movements than a sonata. Sonatinas are usually simpler than sonatas and designed for instruction.

VARIATIONS: A form in which a simple theme (usually in binary form, 16-32 measures, and frequently borrowed from another composer) is followed by modified restatements, each being a "variation."

VIENNESE SONATINA NO. 1

(First movement)

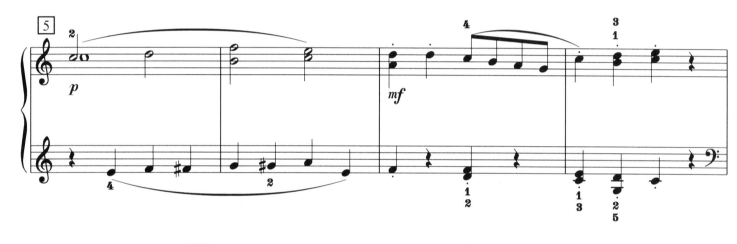

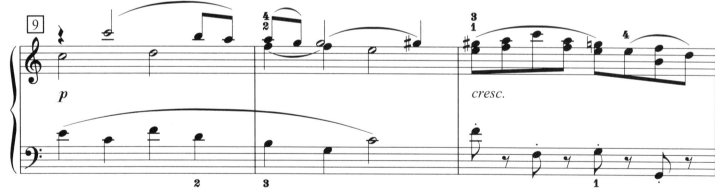

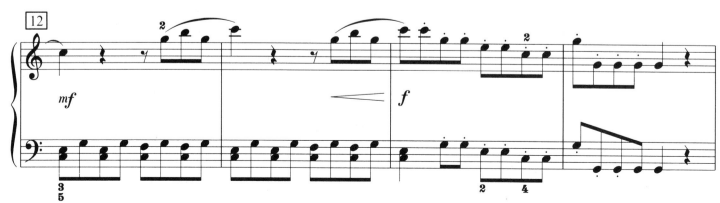

SONATA IN C MAJOR
K. 545

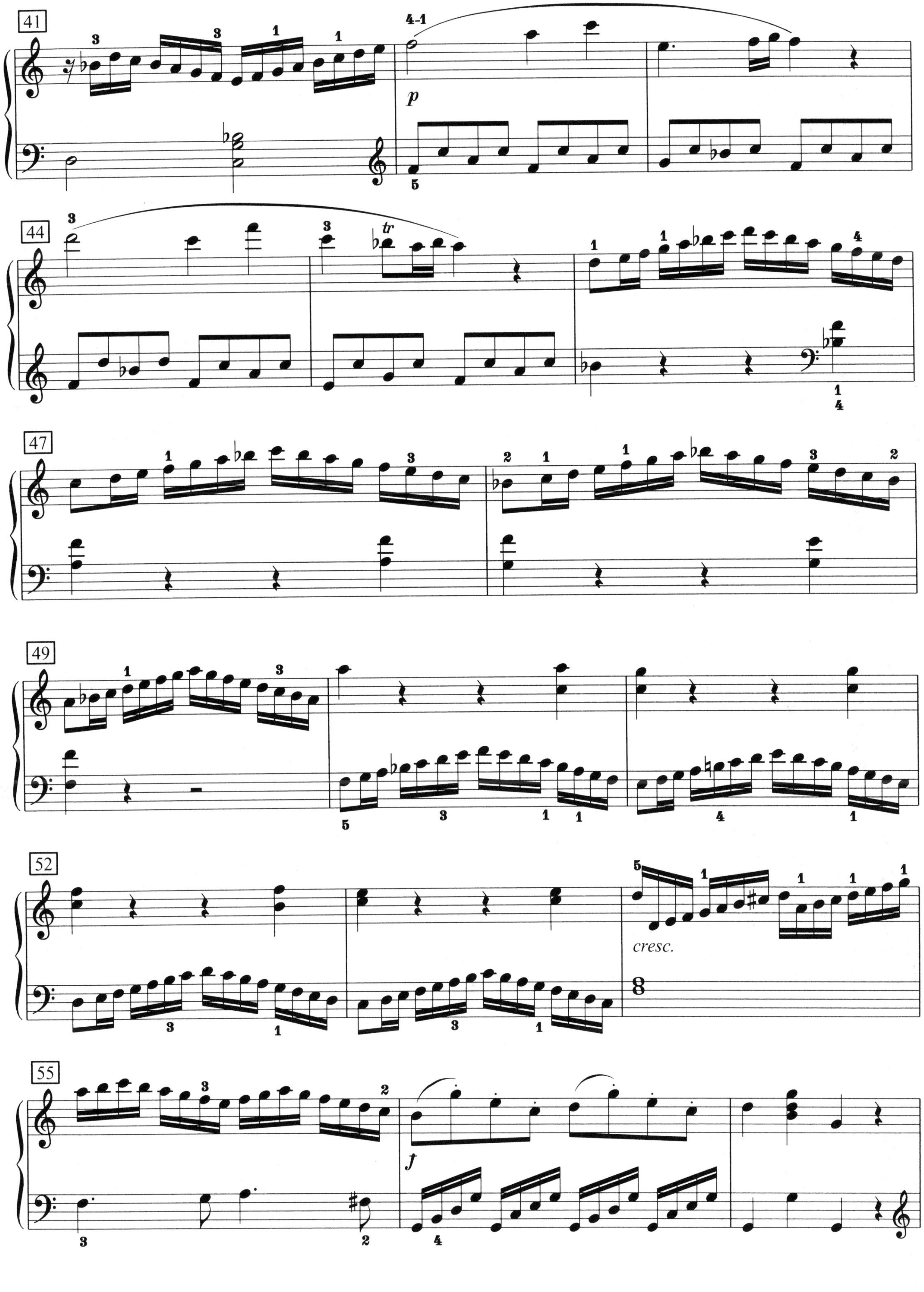
41
44
47
49
52
cresc.
55

14

RONDO
Allegretto

FANTASY IN D MINOR

K. 397

22

GP394

24

RONDO IN D MAJOR

K. 485

cresc.

dim.

TWELVE VARIATIONS ON
"Ah, vous dirai - je Maman"
K. 300e (K. 265)

Theme

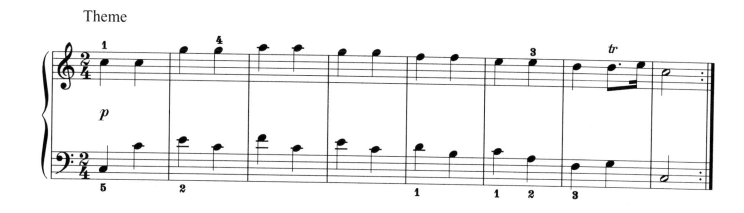

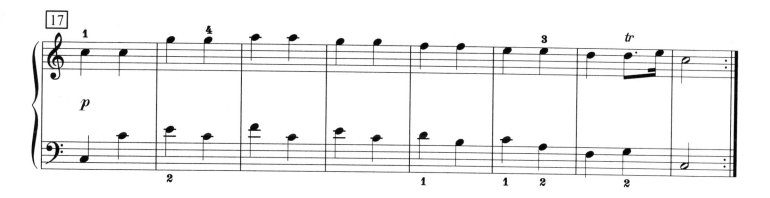

Var. I

Var. II

Var. VI

42

Var. VII

Var. VIII

44

Var. IX

46

Var. XI

Adagio

GP394

Var. XII

Allegro

RONDO ALLA TURCA

from Sonata in A

K. 331